THIS BOOK
BELONGS TO

_____

_____

_____

THE SIMPSONS 2018 ANNUAL

Copyright © 2017
Bongo Entertainment, Inc. All rights reserved.

FIRST EDITION: SEPTEMBER 2017
ISBN 9781785656569

2 4 6 8 10 9 7 5 3 1
Publisher: Matt Groening
Creative Director: Nathan Kane
Managing Editor: Terry Delegeane
Director of Operations: Robert Zaugh
Art Director: Chia-Hsien Jason Ho
Production Manager: Christopher Ungar
Assistant Art Director: Mike Rote
Assistant Editor: Karen Bates
Colors: Art Villanueva
Administration: Ruth Waytz
Legal Guardian: Susan A. Grode

PRINTED IN ITALY

SIMPSONS COMICS ™

MATT GROENING

TITAN BOOKS

MUTINY ON THE BARTY

I CALL IT "STICK AND SLIDE," AND IF I SAY SO MYSELF, IT'S MY *MASTERPIECE*.

THE WHEELS ARE *ALREADY* IN MOTION.

SO WHERE DO *WE* COME IN?

YOU *DON'T*. BUT WHAT GOOD IS A PRANK IF NO ONE KNOWS ITS *AUTHOR*?

SO SHARE, BART! *SHARE!*

CHUCK DIXON & E. BLACKBURN SCRIPT   **JOHN DELANEY** PENCILS   **ANDREW PEPOY** INKS   **ART VILLANUEVA** COLORS   **KAREN BATES** LETTERS   **NATHAN KANE** EDITOR

"TOMORROW, SKINNER WILL SIT DOWN IN HIS OFFICE AFTER MORNING ANNOUNCEMENTS..."

"...TO FIND EVERYTHING IS COVERED WITH SUPERGLUE."

HUH?

RIIIIING!

SKINNERRRR!

SUPERINTENDENT CHALMERS?

I NEED YOU TO FAX ME THE RESULTS OF LAST YEAR'S APTITUDE TESTS.

UM... WHAT?

APTITUDE! NOW, SKINNER!

YES, SIR.

MYRA, CAN YOU HELP ME FIND THE FILES ON THIS YEAR'S APTITUDE TESTS?

LAST YEAR! LAST YEAR, SKINNER!

WHOA!

I DON'T SEE ANYTHING IN MY FAX MACHINE, SKINNER!

JUST A *MOMENT*, SIR!

OW!

OW!

OOF!

ARE YOU DILLY-DALLYING, SKINNER?

cant
y cluedo"

y wants
play again
too!

e
tehes
y sayed
o!!!!

Why no
more game

CLUDo
fun?

but i cant
play cuz so
boring

I
I thought lost

I wanna play
again!! again

me sayed
but daddy said "no"

(daddy boring)

THAT'S THE *LAST* OF THE CARGO, CAP'N MCCALLISTER.

YARR. THEN WE SAIL WITHIN THE *HOUR* FOR EXOTIC PORTS.

FROM RUNAWAYS TO *STOWAWAYS*.

I DON'T *KNOW* ABOUT THIS, BART.

COME ON, WHERE'S YOUR SENSE OF *ADVENTURE*?

I CAN'T FEEL ADVENTUROUS WHEN I'M *HUNGRY*.

WELL, WE *WON'T* STARVE! LOOK AT ALL THIS *FOOD*!

OKRA IN BRINE

CANNED BROCCOLI

D'OH!

CLAMATO JUICE

PICKLED BEETS

HEY! PASTA-TOONS!

LIKE *TONS* OF IT!

EEK! THE CAT?

HOW OLD *IS* THIS SPAGHETTI?

EEK! THE CAT PASTA-TOONS

WE'VE A PAIR OF *JONAHS* ABOARD. THEM STOWAWAY BRATS IS A *CURSE*, SAYS I.

YE'RE *RIGHT!* ME GIRLFRIEND *TEXTED* ME TO TELL ME WE'RE THROUGH!

I BANGED ME *HEAD* ON A HATCHWAY!

ME FANTASY FOOTBALL TEAM IS *TWO* AND TEN!

ALL RIGHT! LAST ONE IN LINE IS A *LUBBER!*

CLEAN YOUR PLATE AND THERE'S *DESSERT!*

HWAAP! HWOORP! HHURL!

SO, *NO* DESSERT THEN?

JONAH!

WHAT'S *THAT* SUPPOSED TO MEAN?

...OH.

AND I'M A JONAH FOR *HIRIN'* YE.

SO... JONAH'S A *BAD* THING?

MEANWHILE, BACK IN SPRINGFIELD...

MISSING BOY
BART SIMPSON

555-0...

LUANN?

MARGE?

LOOK AT YOUR POSTER! MILHOUSE LOOKS SO HANDSOME. AND THOSE TEAR-OFF TABS ARE SUCH A GOOD IDEA.

THANKS!

MISSING
MILHOUSE
VAN HOUTEN
REWARD

MILHOUSE RAN AWAY ALL THE TIME WHEN KIRK AND I WERE SEPARATED

I PUT VELCRO ON THE BACK SO WE CAN RE-USE THEM.

THAT IS SO CLEVER!

HEY! GET YOUR OWN POLE, VAN HOUTEN!

WHY SHOULD I? MY KID NEVER GOT IN TROUBLE TILL HE MET YOUR SON!

SOMETIMES I WISH THEY'D RUN AWAY.

HOW IS THIS HELPING TO FIND BART?

OH, HE'LL COME BACK. HE ALWAYS COMES BACK. HE'S LIKE DON JOHNSON.

OUT ON THE BRINY DEEP...

THIS ONE'S ME *SECOND WIFE*. LOST HER IN A STORM OFF HATTERAS IN '62.

AN' HERE'S ME *FOURTH WIFE*. SHE JUMPED SHIP IN MANILA IN '71.

WHY DOES SHE LOOK LIKE *BETTY RUBBLE*?

THAT'S HOW I LIKE TO *REMEMBER* HER. YARR.

ARR. WE'RE DOWN TO THE *RAISINS* IN THIS TUB O' PARTY MIX.

LEAN TIMES AHEAD, I'M *A-FEARIN'*.

PARTY MIX

HMM...THERE'S A WEEK'S WORTH OF MEAT ON *THESE* BONES.

THANKS. I'VE BEEN DOING *PILATES* WITH MY MOM.

FORGET IT! WE'RE *NOT* EATING MY BEST FRIEND...

YEAH!

...UNTIL IT'S *ABSOLUTELY* NECESSARY.

WAIT... *WHAT?*

HEY! LOOK *THERE!*

ESPECIALLY **COMPARED** TO THE MISERABLE HOVEL YOU TWO SLAPPED T'GETHER.

I'D LIKE TO SEE **YOU** DO ANY BETTER, NEMO.

ISLAND LIVING

I NEVER THOUGHT THIS FATE WOULD BEFALL ME **AGAIN**.

YEA, I'VE BEEN MAROONED BEFORE, AND IT ENDED IN BITTER TRAGEDY. YARR.

SHIPWRECKED **TWICE**. THAT'S GOT TO BE **TOUGH**, HUH?

YOU KNOW, I FEEL LIKE THIS HAS HAPPENED TO US ONCE BEFORE.

ONLY IF YOU COUNT "DAS BUS" IN SEASON NINE -- EDITOR

DON'T GIVE UP THE **SHIP**, SKIPPER.

IF I **HAD** ME A SHIP, I WOULDN'T HAVE ME A PROBLEM!

WELL, WHY NOT BUILD A **BOAT**? WE COULD **SAIL** AWAY FROM HERE!

WHO'D BE ME **CREW** THEN?

I'D NEED **MORE** ABLE-BODIED BODIES THAN YOU TWO LADS.

A CREW! **YARR!** I'VE AN **IDEA**, BOYOS! WE'LL--

CLONK!

OWR!

WHAT'S YOUR *IDEA*, CAP'N?

OOOOOO...

PLEASE *TELL* US!

LATER THAT DAY...

YARR! LAY THAT *KEEL* DOWN! THIS VESSEL NEEDS T' BE SHIPSHAPE AND *BRISTOL* FASHION!

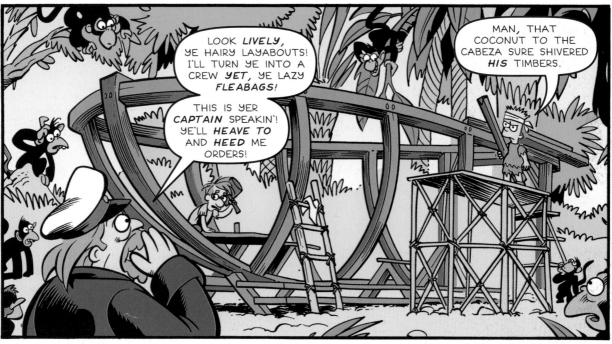

LOOK *LIVELY*, YE HAIRY LAYABOUTS! I'LL TURN YE INTO A CREW *YET*, YE LAZY *FLEABAGS*!

THIS IS YER *CAPTAIN* SPEAKIN'! YE'LL *HEAVE TO* AND *HEED* ME ORDERS!

MAN, THAT COCONUT TO THE CABEZA SURE SHIVERED *HIS* TIMBERS.

THOSE MONKEYS ARE TOO *DUMB* TO HELP US BUILD THE BOAT.

THEY'RE DUMB? LOOK WHO'S DOING ALL THE *WORK*.

I WISH WE WERE BACK IN SPRINGFIELD. ⦂SIGH.⦂ YOU THINK OUR PARENTS ARE STILL *LOOKING* FOR US?

ARE YOU *KIDDING*? THEY'LL *NEVER* GIVE UP THE SEARCH.

YEAH...

BACK IN SPRINGFIELD...

MISSING

MISSING

WE'RE CALLING OFF THE SEARCH!

IT'S BEEN A WEEK, THERE'S NO SIGN OF THE BOYS, AND THERE'S NO MORE MONEY IN THE CITY BUDGET TO KEEP LOOKING.

I BLAME THE RECESSION.

WHAT ABOUT THE RUMORS THAT THE POLICE DEPARTMENT USED FUNDS ALLOTED FOR THE SEARCH ON *EXTRAVAGANT* PURCHASES?

PRESS

THAT HURTS.

ALL OUR MONEY GOES TOWARD LEGITIMATE CRIME PREVENTION SUPPLIES.

AND *NOTHING* PREVENTS CRIME LIKE THE *ORIGINAL* BATMOBILE!

THESE PEOPLE WOULDN'T LAST FIVE *MINUTES* BEHIND THE BADGE.

OH NO! THEY'RE *GIVING UP* ON MY LITTLE BARTY!

DON'T WORRY, MARGE! BART STILL HAS *LOVED ONES* TO LOOK FOR HIM.

I'LL BEGIN THE SEARCH AT *MOE'S!*

TWEET ME IF HE TURNS UP, OKAY?

BACK ON MONKEY ISLAND...

THE *SKIPPER* SAYS WE SET SAIL AT HIGH TIDE TOMORROW.

THINK ABOUT IT, MILHOUSE. WE'LL BE JUST LIKE *JOHNNY DEPP*.

YEAH...

IT'LL BE GREAT TO BE BACK HOME. YOU KNOW WHO *I* MISS THE MOST?

≥SHUDDER!≤

SOMETHING *WRONG*, LISA?

ALL STORES *ABOARD*, SIR!

ARE WE READY FOR *LAUNCH*, SKIPPER?

AYE...

...BUT I HATE LEAVIN' SO MANY *ABLE* HANDS BEHIND.

THE END

MAGGIE'S CRIB

by ARAGONÉS

SERGIO ARAGONÉS
STORY & ART

NATHAN HAMILL
COLORS

BILL MORRISON
EDITOR

ALIENATED!

ICHOR-FILLED
IAN BOOTHBY
WRITER

TERRIFYING
TONE RODRIGUEZ
PENCILS

ARCANE
ANDREW PEPOY
INKS

NUMB
NATHAN HAMILL
COLORS

KREEPY
KAREN BATES
LETTERS

NORMAL
NATHAN KANE
EDITOR

BUT DON'T YOU THINK IT'S *STRANGE* THAT THE NEW LUNCH LADIES NEVER COME OUT OF THE KITCHEN?

SELF SERVE (DON'T BOTHER US!)

EH, I THINK ABOUT THE LUNCH LADIES ABOUT AS MUCH AS I THINK ABOUT *THE JANITOR!*

:SOB!:

THIS IS GOOD. MAYBE *TOO* GOOD! I'LL BET IT'S FULL OF CHEMICALS AND ADDITIVES! I'D BETTER HAVE IT CHECKED OUT!

MILK

LATER...

THANKS FOR EXAMINING THIS FOOD, PROFESSOR FRINK. WAS I RIGHT? HAS IT BEEN GENETICALLY MODIFIED?

FRINK LABS
WHERE THE FUTURE IS BEING MADE TOMORROW!

DON'T WORRY, LITTLE GIRL. THIS ISN'T G.M.O.* FOOD!

*GENETICALLY MODIFIED ORGANISM—EDITOR NATHAN

IT'S *U.F.O.* *FOOD!*

NONE OF THE INGREDIENTS ARE FOUND ON EARTH! IT'S MADE OF *POWERFUL MUTAGENS!* ¦GA-HOY!¦

*WHAT THE WHAT?!—EDITOR NATHAN

YOU MUST LET ME RUN A *SERIES OF TESTS* ON YOU!

OOOH! TESTS!

SOON...

SWEET GLAVIN'S BEARD! IT'S JUST AS I SUSPECTED!

ALONG WITH OTHER PHYSICAL CHANGES, THE FOOD IS RAISING YOUR INTELLIGENCE ONE I.Q. POINT A MINUTE!

HERE'S THE PROOF! NOW GO AND TELL THE WORLD! THIS MUST BE *STOPPED!*

I *WILL,* PROFESSOR!

BUT MAYBE NOT RIGHT AWAY!

OUR SCHOOL COULD *USE* A LITTLE SMARTENING UP!

TOSS!

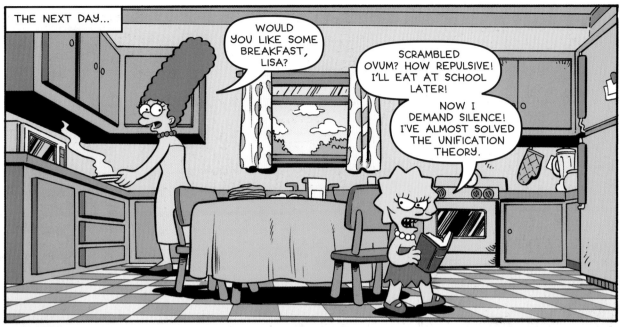

THE NEXT DAY...

WOULD YOU LIKE SOME BREAKFAST, LISA?

SCRAMBLED OVUM? HOW REPULSIVE! I'LL EAT AT SCHOOL LATER!

NOW I DEMAND SILENCE! I'VE ALMOST SOLVED THE UNIFICATION THEORY.

HOMER, I'M WORRIED ABOUT BART AND LISA! THEY'VE BEEN ACTING ODDLY. *DROOLING* ALL THE TIME AND *QUICK TO ANGER*.

I DON'T KNOW WHERE THEY GET *THAT* FROM.

MMMMMM... BACON!

DROOL!

HI-DIDDLY HO, HOMER! WE GOT SOME OF YOUR MAIL BY MISTAKE!

GRRR! GET LOST, FLANDERS!

AND THEY'VE BOTH GOTTEN SO SMART.

MARGE! I PUT BACON IN MY POCKETS AND NOW THE DOG'S GOT MY PANTS!

OKAY, SO IT MIGHT NOT BE HEREDITARY.

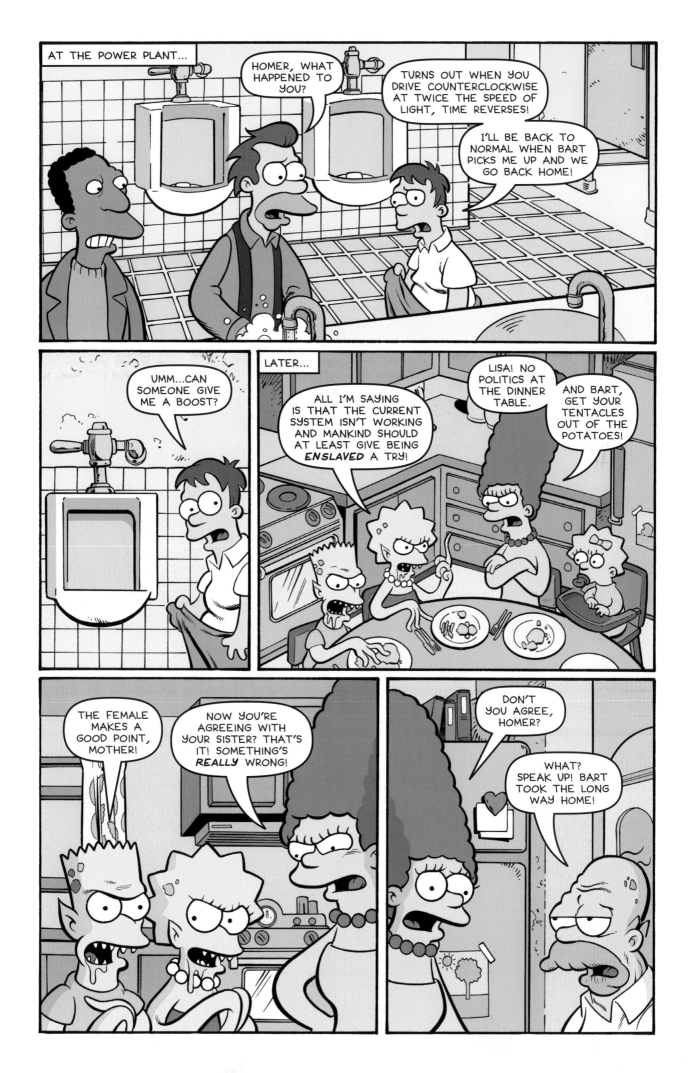

SOME DAYS LATER...

AND SO I CALL TOGETHER THE FIRST MEETING OF *CONCERNED RESPONSIBLE ADULT PARENTS!*

FIRST ORDER OF BUSINESS...

...CAN WE CHANGE OUR NAME?

NO!

C.R.A.P.

AS YOU MAY BE AWARE, OUR CHILDREN HAVE BEEN GETTING *OUT OF CONTROL* LATELY!

THEY'RE ALSO TURNING GREEN AND GROWING FANGS, TENTACLES, AND A GIANT EYEBALL!

WORSE THAN THE PHYSICAL CHANGES IS THE ATTITUDE AND *SASS MOUTH!* ROD AND TODD HAVE TAKEN TO ANSWERING ME BY USING THE WORD "WHATEVER!"

ALSO, I THINK THEY'RE MUTILATING CATTLE.

RALPHIE STARTED PLAYING HIS SO-CALLED "MUSIC" DAY AND NIGHT. MY EARS HAVEN'T STOPPED BLEEDING FOR A WEEK!

UMM...I'M GONNA CHANGE SEATS, CHIEF.

AND SEYMOUR KEEPS DISAPPOINTING ME!

BUT *I* HAVEN'T CHANGED, MOTHER.

DON'T I KNOW IT.

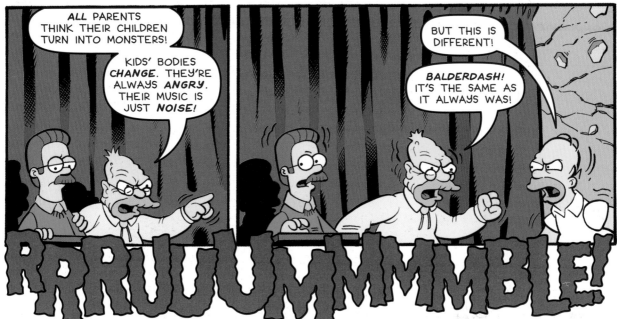

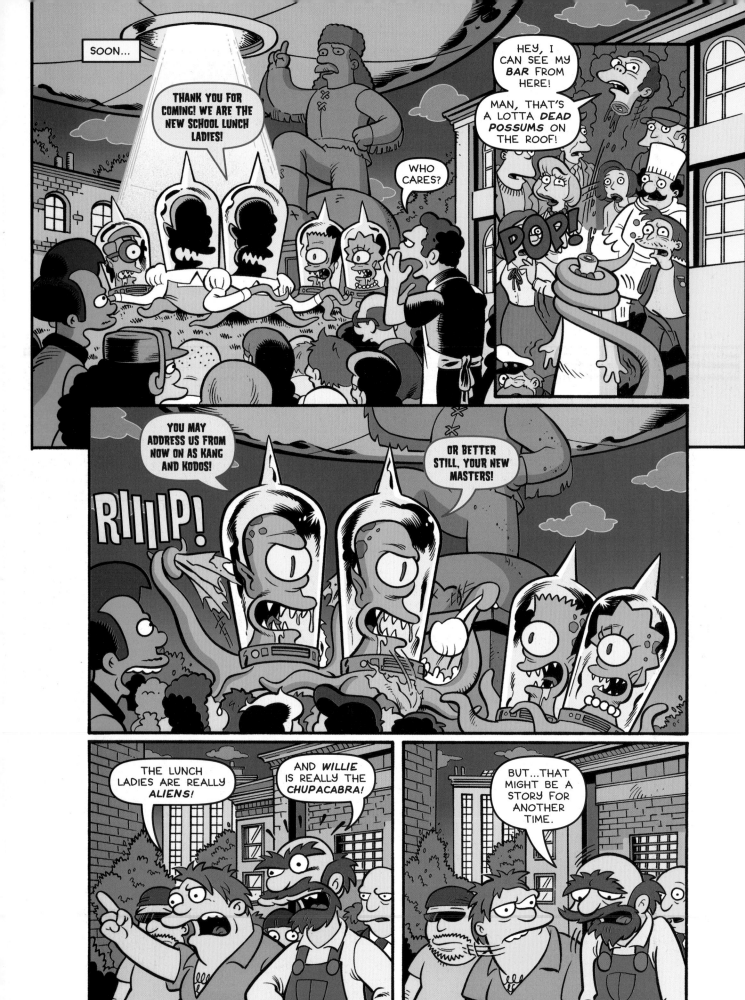

GOOD COP, BART COP!

SO WHAT CAUSED THE RIOT?

THIS PUNK CONVINCED A BIRTHDAY PARTY OF FIVE-YEAR-OLDS THAT OUR KRUSTY KIDS' MEALS WERE MADE WITH *REAL KIDS*!

I WAS JUST TELLING THEM WHAT THE INTERNET TOLD ME.

THE ONLY KIDS WE USE ARE *GOATS*... AND THAT'S JUST THEIR *HORNS*! WE GRIND THEM UP AS *SEASONING* IN THE CURLY FRIES!

IAN BOOTHBY	**JOHN DELANEY**	**ANDREW PEPOY**	**NATHAN HAMILL**	**KAREN BATES**	**NATHAN KANE**
SCRIPT	PENCILS	INKS	COLORS	LETTERS	EDITOR

LATER...

THIS IS YOUR *THIRTIETH STRIKE*, BART! HERE'S THE DEAL. YOU CAN GO TO JUVENILE HALL...

¡GULP!¡

...OR YOU CAN JOIN THE POLICE IN A *NEW CRIME-FIGHTING DIVISION* CALLED "*KID COPS!*"

SAY *WHAT* NOW?

HI, PARTNER!

RALPHIE'S BIRTHDAY WISH WAS TO BE A POLICE OFFICER, BUT I DON'T WANT HIM DOING THIS ALONE...HE'S NOT THE BRIGHTEST BULB IN THE PACK!

OW! QUIT IT!

GRRR! I'M TAKING A *BITE* OUT OF CRIME!

SO *THAT'S* MY CHOICE? JUVIE OR HANGING OUT WITH RALPH?

WELL?

I'M THINKING, I'M THINKING!

AND SO...

♪ WE'RE ON PATROL! WE'RE ON PATROL! HEIGH-HO THE DERRY-O! WE'RE ON ♪ PATROL! ♪

I GUESS THIS ISN'T SO BAD. HOW MANY *KID CRIMES* CAN THERE BE?

I GOT THE CHOCOLATE OUT, BUT I THINK THERE'S STILL SOME RAISINS UP THERE!

I'LL TELL YOU EVERYTHING!

ONE CONFESSION LATER...

ONE MORE THING...

...MY DAD SENT A *JELLY DONUT BOMB* TO THE POLICE STATION. I WAS GOING TO USE IT TO ESCAPE.

HERE'S YOUR CONFESSION, DADDY!

WOW! GREAT WORK! I'M SO *PROUD* OF YOU!

OH, BUT DON'T EAT THOSE JELLY DONUTS! ONE OF THEM'S A BOMB!

BART, YOU'VE DONE MORE THAN ENOUGH TO MAKE UP YOUR DEBT TO SOCIETY! YOU DON'T HAVE TO BE A KID COP ANYMORE!

ALL RIGHT!

...

ʅSIGH!ʃ

YOU KNOW WHAT, CHIEF? THIS CITY COULD USE SOME MORE CLEANING UP! I THINK I'LL STAY A KID COP A WHILE LONGER!

YAY! IT'S *KID COPS TWO! THE SQUEAKQUEL!*

COP OUT!

PRANKENSTEIN'S MONSTER!

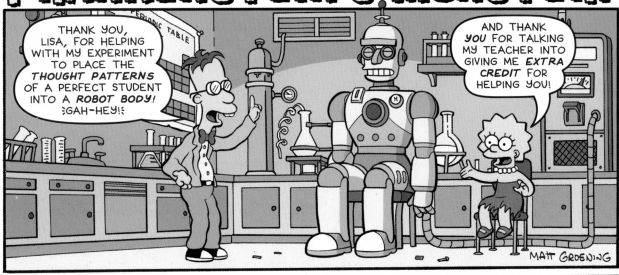

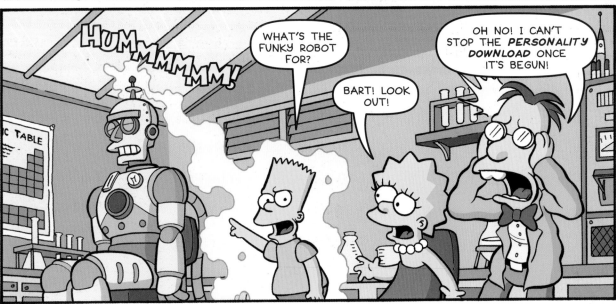

IAN BOOTHBY WRITER   **JAMES LLOYD** PENCILS   **ANDREW PEPOY** INKS   **NATHAN HAMILL** COLORS   **KAREN BATES** LETTERS   **NATHAN KANE** EDITOR

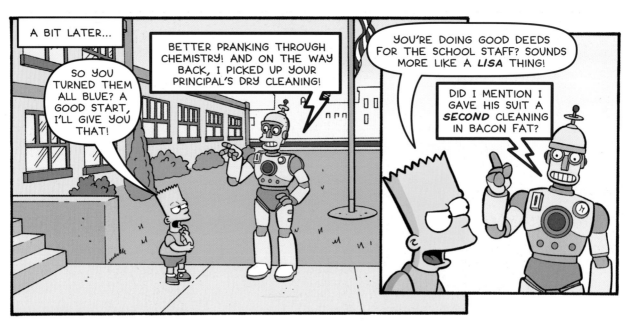

THE NEXT DAY...

OH, I'LL FIGHT THE FUTURE ALL RIGHT. AND WHEN I'M DONE, THE FUTURE'LL WISH IT NEVER MESSED WITH BART SIMPSON!

HEH HEH! THE OLD *SUPERGLUE ON THE TEACHER'S CHAIR GAG!* CLASSIC!

NOT BAD FOR A SMART HUMAN LIKE YOU! BEING A SIMPLE ROBOT, I JUST PUT GLUE ON THE *ENTIRE DESK!*

YAAAH!

AW NUTS! MY PANTS ARE STUCK!

RRRIP!

BRRRRING!

OH NO! THE BELL!

QUICK! JUMP OUT THE WINDOW BEFORE YOUR CLASS-MATES COME IN!

A FEW DAYS LATER...

BART, WHY ARE YOU READING A *MATH BOOK*? ARE YOU GOING TO USE ARITHMETIC IN A PRANK AGAINST THAT ROBOT?

NAH, I KNOW WHEN I'M BEAT. EVERYONE'S POSTED THOSE PICTURES OF ME ON THEIR *MYFACE PAGES*.

I HAVE MORE HITS THAN THAT CAT WHO EATS A CHEESEBURGER WHILE PLAYING THE PIANO!

CLASH OF THE TITANS
RAY HARRYHAUSEN

THE BETTER PRANKSTER WON. PROFESSOR FRINK WAS RIGHT. YOU *CAN'T* FIGHT THE FUTURE.

I DIDN'T HAVE ANYTHING ELSE TO DO, SO I'M STUDYING.

WELL, I GUESS I'M GLAD TO HEAR THAT. MAYBE OVER TIME YOU'LL EVEN START TO DO AS WELL IN SCHOOL AS ME.

I GOT STRAIGHT "A"S ON MY LAST THREE TESTS.

YOU *WHAT*?!

OH NO! THE WATER IS SHORTING HIM OUT!

ALERT! SYSTEM FAILURE! REBOOTING HARD DRIVE! ASSIMILATING NEAREST BRAINWAVES!

ARE YOU ALL RIGHT?

SWEET GLAVIN, AM I *EVER!* WITH THE INCREASED BRAINPOWER AND THE NEW SUPER-THINKING!

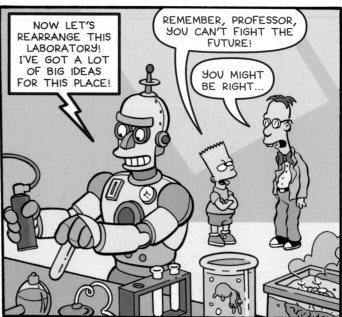

WHY DO YOU SOUND SO MUCH MORE INTELLIGENT?

HOW ELSE SHOULD YOUR REPLACEMENT SOUND? ⁞GAY-HEY!⁞ MEET THE *FRINKBOT 5000!*

NOW LET'S REARRANGE THIS LABORATORY! I'VE GOT A LOT OF BIG IDEAS FOR THIS PLACE!

REMEMBER, PROFESSOR, YOU CAN'T FIGHT THE FUTURE!

YOU MIGHT BE RIGHT...

...BUT WE'LL JUST SEE HOW THE FUTURE STANDS UP TO A *BALL-PEEN HAMMER!*

⁞GAH-HOYVEN!⁞ LET'S NOT MAKE WITH THE HITTING, NICE, INFERIOR HUMAN-TYPE PERSON!

THE PRANK MASTER TITLE IS MINE ONCE AGAIN! HOW CAN I THANK YOU?

NEVER GET A HIGHER GRADE THAN A "B+" AND DON'T EVER PLAY THE SAXOPHONE AGAIN!

DEAL!

THE FRINKIN' END!

SPRINGFIELD STORIES!

MMMM... EXPLOSIVE!

TITAN BOOKS
A WORLD OF ENTERTAINMENT

www.titanbooks.com